THIS BOOK BELONGS TO

**BATMAN ANNUAL 2014**



Published in the UK by Titan Comics, a division of Titan Publishing Group Ltd,
144 Southwark St, London SE1 0UP.



First edition: August 2013
ISBN: 978-1-78276-027-6
TCN: 0098
10 9 8 7 6 5 4 3 2 1

A CIP catalogue record for this title is available from the British Library.



**PRINTED IN ITALY**

# BATMAN™

# ANNUAL 2014

TITAN COMICS

**BATMAN: THE MOVIE** part 1 of 1

WRITTEN BY ANDREW DABB
ART BY GIORGIO PONTRELLI
COLORS BY ANTONIO FABELA
LETTERS BY SAIDA TEMOFONTE
COVER BY JHEREMY RAAPACK AND LOPEZ & CASAS OF IKARI STUDIO
ASSOCIATE EDITOR KRISTY QUINN
EDITOR BEN ABERNATHY
BATMAN CREATED BY BOB KANE

LOOK, THIS AIN'T EXACTLY SHAKESPEARE, I ADMIT.
BUT BAT-MAN, THERE'S A REASON HE MAKES THE PAPERS, THE BLOGS, THE... TWEETERS, OR WHATEVER.
HE ***MEANS*** SOMETHIN' TO PEOPLE.

BAT-MAN'S LIKE...WE ALL GOT SOME DOUCHE IN OUR LIFE WE WISH WE COULD PUNCH IN THE TEETH.
AND THE BAT-- HE TAKES DOWN WHOEVER. THEY GOT IT COMIN', HE HANDS 'EM THEIR ASS.

AND THAT'S WHY THIS PICTURE'S GONNA BE A FOUR-QUADRANT BLOCKBUSTER, OKAY?
SO...HE'S AN EXPRESSION OF OUR COLLECTIVE UNCONSCIOUS?
SURE, SOUNDS GOOD TO ME.

NOW COME ON, LET'S GO BLOW SOME CRAP UP.

ALL RIGHT, WE'RE IN THE TOWERING INFERNO SCENE.
THE GREEN SCREEN WILL ALL BE FIRE, ONCE WE DO THE CGI.

THAT TENNIS BALL? IT'S THE PENGUIN-COPTER.
AND LARRY OVER THERE, HE'S THE PENGUIN. OR HE WILL BE, WHEN *WETA* DOES THEIR THING.
COLIN! ERIC!

MEET *BRUCE WAYNE.*

MR. WAYNE'S FOUNDATION OWNS THIS BUILDING, HE ASKED TO VISIT THE SET.
ACTUALLY, I ASKED TO MEET YOUR CO-STAR. THOUGHT I'D GIVE HER A FRIENDLY WELCOME TO GOTHAM.
JENNY'S IN HER TRAILER. AND *MARRIED.*

*US WEEKLY* SAYS IT'S ON THE ROCKS.
*US WEEKLY* CAN KISS MY--

COLIN, TIME TO SUIT UP.

BEAUTIFUL CITY YOU GOT HERE, MR. WAYNE.
I MEAN, WE COULDA FILMED THIS THING CHEAPER IN VANCOUVER, BELIEVE ME.
BUT GOTHAM, IT'S THE BAT'S STOMPIN' GROUND-- HIS HOME TURF.
WE HAD TO USE IT.
'CAUSE THAT'S WHAT WE'RE ABOUT, BRUCE--
AUTHENTICITY.

SO, WHATCHA THINK?
VERY... LITERAL.

HAVE YOU EVER SEEN THE BAT-MAN?
I SAW A GIRL DRESSED AS SLUTTY BAT-MAN LAST HALLOWEEN, DOES THAT COUNT?

THIS WAY, BRUCE.
JERK.

ALL RIGHT, QUIET ON THE SET! PLACES!
ACTION--!
AND CUT!
LADIES, GENTLEMEN, BOYS AND GIRLS OF ALL AGES.
I'VE TAKEN THE LIBERTY OF STASHING A DOZEN HIGHLY EXPLOSIVE PARTY FAVORS ALL AROUND YOU.
SO NO ONE MOVES, OR EVERYONE GOES BOOM.
WHAT ARE YOU?
I'M BAT-MAN.
REALLY? BECAUSE... REALLY?
DOESN'T MATTER.
IT'S TIME FOR FAME, FORTUNE AND GLAMOUR, WITH AN EXTRA HELPING OF GLITZ.
IT'S TIME TO MAKE A MOVIE-- MY MOVIE.

THE REST OF YOU WILL KEEP THOSE CAMERAS ROLLING NO MATTER WHAT. UNDERSTAND?

YOU'RE HARLEY QUINN?
ONE AND ONLY, SUGAH.

I DON'T--WHY ARE YOU DOING THIS?
WHY DOES ANYONE? US, THE CAPES...
...'CAUSE IT'S *FUN*, AND WE GET TO DRESS UP.

OR WE'RE ALL JUST PSYCHO. OR BOTH.
HARLEY!

READY FOR YOUR CLOSE-UP, MACKEREL?
SURE AM, MISTAH J! WHERE'S MY SCRIPT?
NO SCRIPT, JUST A TITLE.

*THE DEATH OF BATMAN.*

WHAM
OOH! A SPECIAL GUEST STAR!
ACTION JACKSON!
KRAK
TSK. TOLD HER NOT TO DO HER OWN STUNTS.
DROP THE DETONATOR, JOKER. I'VE DISARMED ALL TWELVE OF YOUR BOMBS.
TWELVE? OH...DID I FORGET TO MENTION LUCKY NUMBER THIRTEEN?
BOOM

UHH...
GET UP.
ARE YOU OKAY--
MOVE.

BATS! I DIDN'T SAY CUT!
AND I'M GONNA CUT, AND CUT, AND CUT!
WHAT DO WE DO?
PSSS
TRUST ME.

AW, POOR BABY.
YOUR FRIEND, TOM SNOOZE, HE'S A CURIOUS KITTEN.
WANTED TO KNOW THE ANSWER TO THE BIGGEST BIG QUESTION OF ALL: *WHY?*

I COULD HAVE TOLD HIM: THESE ARE THE ROLES WE WERE BORN TO PLAY.
AFTER ALL, WHAT'S LIFE BUT ONE BIG MOVIE? YOU'RE THE HERO--TORTURED, GRIM, *SO SAD.* AND I'M THE VILLAIN, BUT THAT'S OKAY.
THE BAD GUY GETS ALL THE *BEST LINES.*

WE MOVE FROM SET PIECE TO SET PIECE, CHASING McGUFFINS, TEASING AN ENDING NEITHER OF US REALLY WANT.
WHY WOULD WE? THIS FLICK, IT'S A *HIT.*

BATS... WHEN DID YOU GO *BLONDE?*

HHH...

WHAT HAPPENED?
YOU MISSED THE CLIMAX, BUT YOU'RE JUST IN TIME FOR THE RESOLUTION.

YOU ALL RIGHT?
I'M-- I THINK SO.
I JUST-- HELP ME UNDERSTAND. WHY DO YOU DO THIS?

GOOD LUCK WITH YOUR MOVIE.

THE END

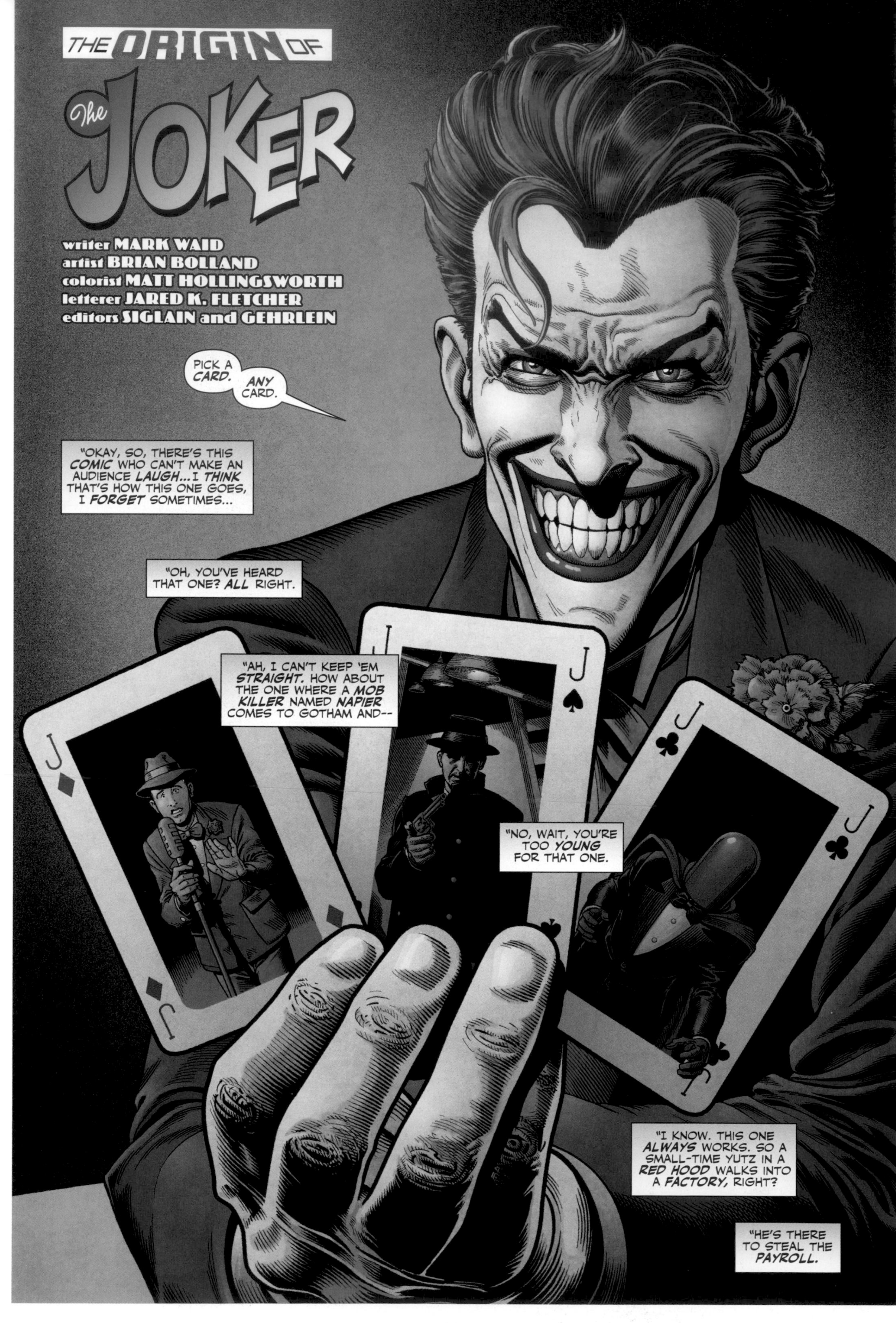
THE ORIGIN OF
The JOKER
writer MARK WAID
artist BRIAN BOLLAND
colorist MATT HOLLINGSWORTH
letterer JARED K. FLETCHER
editors SIGLAIN and GEHRLEIN
PICK A CARD.
ANY CARD.
"OKAY, SO, THERE'S THIS COMIC WHO CAN'T MAKE AN AUDIENCE LAUGH...I THINK THAT'S HOW THIS ONE GOES, I FORGET SOMETIMES...
"OH, YOU'VE HEARD THAT ONE? ALL RIGHT.
"AH, I CAN'T KEEP 'EM STRAIGHT. HOW ABOUT THE ONE WHERE A MOB KILLER NAMED NAPIER COMES TO GOTHAM AND--
"NO, WAIT, YOU'RE TOO YOUNG FOR THAT ONE.
"I KNOW. THIS ONE ALWAYS WORKS. SO A SMALL-TIME YUTZ IN A RED HOOD WALKS INTO A FACTORY, RIGHT?
"HE'S THERE TO STEAL THE PAYROLL.

## Powers & Weapons:

THE JOKER HAS NO SPECIAL POWERS, BUT HIS UNIQUE PSYCHOSES MAKE HIM THE MOST DANGEROUS KILLER IN THE WORLD. HIS CHIEF WEAPON IS JOKER VENOM, A FATAL TOXIN THAT KILLS ITS VICTIMS ON CONTACT--BUT NOT BEFORE SENDING THEM INTO FITS OF SICK LAUGHTER AND LOCKING THEIR FACES INTO A SMILING DEATH RICTUS.

## Essential Storylines:

- BATMAN: THE KILLING JOKE
- BATMAN: A DEATH IN THE FAMILY
- JOKER: THE DEVIL'S ADVOCATE
- BATMAN: THE MAN WHO LAUGHS

SPACE.
I HATE SPACE. IT CAN KILL YOU IN UNDER A MINUTE.
ROUGH ESTIMATE.
IT'S AIRLESS. SUB-ZERO TEMPERATURES.
NO PRESSURE.
LENSES PROTECT THE EYES. REBREATHER'S GOT NO AIR, BUT THE PRESSURE SEAL BUYS ME ANOTHER MINUTE.
AFTER THAT, IT'S EASY. JLA SIGNAL DEVICE HAS TELEPORTER CONTROLS BUILT IN.
WATER VAPOR'S FROZEN ON THE CONTROLS. SLIPPERY.
ENTER COORDINATES
OOPS.

A MINUTE AGO I WAS BACK ON THE SATELLITE.
HATE SATELLITES, TOO.
BUT WHAT I REALLY HATE? TELEPORTERS.
TELEPORT: INCOMING.
WHY DO I HATE TELEPORTERS?
UNINVITED GUESTS.
INCOMING TELEPORT: COMPLETE.
AND YET...A SEEMINGLY EMPTY TELEPORTER BAY.

SOMEONE GOT IN THE SATELLITE UNSEEN.

WHO COULD GET IN HERE...FROM OUT THERE? POSSIBILITIES...
INVISIBILITY. METAMORPHOSIS. MAGIC. MIND CONTROL. SUPER-SPEED. NONE OF THE ABOVE.

OR...

...ALL OF THE ABOVE.
AMAZO. SENTIENT ANDROID POSSESSING ALL THE LEAGUE'S SUPERPOWERS.

COMPUTER: INITIATE AMAZO PROTOC--

UFF!
PLAN B.

SO MUCH FOR THE ALARM.
BE RIGHT WITH YOU.

PLAN C.

I LOCKED IT. BREACH THE AIRLOCK AND AN AUTOMATED ALARM SUMMONS THEM.
THE AMAZON. THE ALIENS. ALL OF THEM.

THAT'S WHY I'M TAKING YOU OUT ONE BY ONE THIS TIME. STARTING WITH THE POWERLESS ONE. THE ONE I CAN KILL WITH THE PRESS OF A BUTTON.

OPEN EXTERNAL

THINK YOU CAN KILL ME? THINK I'M POWERLESS?
THINK AGAIN.

COMPUTER: ACCESS MEMBER FILES. COMPILE DATABASE OF KNOWN LIMITATIONS ON EXTRA-HUMAN CAPABILITIES.
YES, J'ONN.

HA! AT LEAST YOU GOT A SHOT IN, GREEN--

NOW WHAT?
HEAT? I FLY THROUGH SUNS AND YOU ATTACK ME BY TURNING UP THE *THERMOSTAT?*
THIS IS SOME STUPID PROGRAM HE LEFT BEHIND TO MAKE ME THINK HE'S STILL ALIVE.
--ARROW?
THINK AGAIN!

NEXT TIME I KILL YOU--YOU *STAY* DEAD!

THINK AGAIN
THINK AGAIN


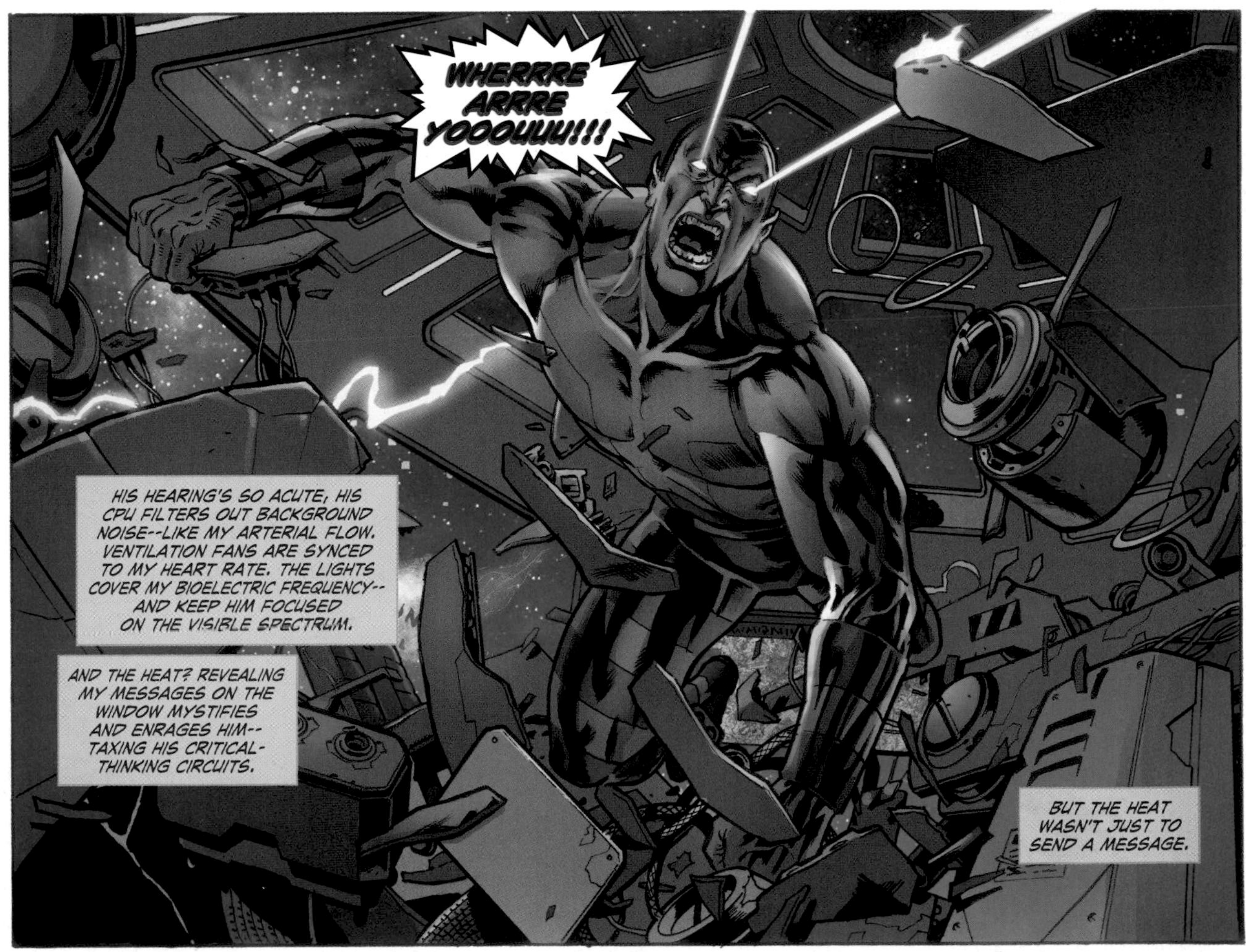

WHERRRE ARRRE YOOOUUU!!!
HIS HEARING'S SO ACUTE; HIS CPU FILTERS OUT BACKGROUND NOISE--LIKE MY ARTERIAL FLOW. VENTILATION FANS ARE SYNCED TO MY HEART RATE. THE LIGHTS COVER MY BIOELECTRIC FREQUENCY--AND KEEP HIM FOCUSED ON THE VISIBLE SPECTRUM.
AND THE HEAT? REVEALING MY MESSAGES ON THE WINDOW MYSTIFIES AND ENRAGES HIM--TAXING HIS CRITICAL-THINKING CIRCUITS.
BUT THE HEAT WASN'T JUST TO SEND A MESSAGE.

I SET THE THERMOSTAT AT 101.2 TO MASK MY HEAT SIGNATURE.
RUNNING A SLIGHT FEVER.
SO NOW HE TURNS TO X-RAY VISION.
THE NON-SUPER HUMAN'S BEST FRIEND.
THEY NEVER SEEM TO FIGURE IT OUT...
...WHEN YOU CAN LOOK THROUGH EVERYTHING, YOU CAN'T SEE ANYTHING.

AMAZO'S CREATOR SAW THE PROBLEM, SO HE PROGRAMMED AMAZO TO SCAN ONE LAYER AT A TIME.
AMAZO COMPARES THE SCAN RESULTS TO HIS SEARCH PARAMETERS. FOR INSTANCE: A UNIFORM.

POWER GIRL
GREEN ARROW
BOOSTER GOLD
GREEN LANTERN
BATMAN
SUPERMAN
BUT THEN HE'S GOT TO CONFIRM. SO HE SCANS THE NEXT LEVEL IN.

AND WHEN HE SEES IT'S JUST A STATUE...

...HE'S DONE.

J'ONN ONCE TOLD ME WHEN PEOPLE THINK HARD, HE AND CLARK CAN HEAR THE NEURONS FIRE. SODIUM IONS PERMEATING CELL MEMBRANES.
I DID MY THINKING BEFORE MY LITTLE SPACEWALK. SO NOW, WHEN I'M READY FOR HIM...

...I THINK AGAIN.

THE TRICK TO STOPPING A SPEEDSTER? TALK. THEY ALWAYS WAIT TO HEAR WHAT YOU'RE SAYING.
YOU'RE WONDERING HOW I GOT BACK IN. I'LL TELL YOU.

"I HAD A TELEPORTER CONTROLLER ON ME. BUT I DROPPED IT.
"HAD TO ESTIMATE TRAJECTORY AND SPEED BEFORE IT GOT TOO FAR. CALCULATE AN INTERCEPT COURSE.
ENTER COORDINATES

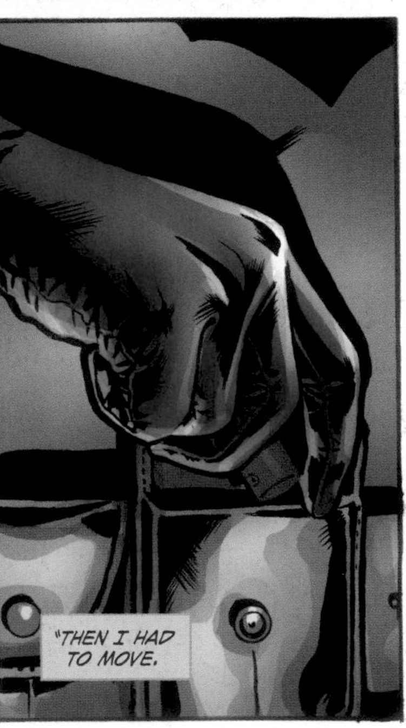
"THEN I HAD TO MOVE.

"BAT-SHARK REPELLANT.
YOU'RE DOING GREAT, THOUGH.
MAYBE NEXT TIME YOU CAN TRY PLASTIC MAN.
EXECUTE PROGRAM
DIE NOW!
AS LONG AS YOU KEEP TALKING, YOU CAN DO WHAT YOU WANT...
...LIKE REPROGRAM A TELEPORTER.
IN SOME CIRCLES, DOING TWO THINGS AT ONCE COUNTS AS A SUPER POWER.
NO!
AMAZO HAS ALL THE POWERS OF ALL THE SUPERHUMANS IN THE JUSTICE LEAGUE. HIS ONLY WEAKNESS IS...

...HE DOESN'T HAVE MINE.

HE'LL BE BACK, THOUGH.

MULTIPLE TELEPORTS: SENT.
IF ANYONE CAN FIND ALL THE PIECES.

HAVE TO FIX THE GLITCH THAT LET AMAZO IN ON THE TELEPORTER-- MISTAKING HIM FOR THE OTHER MEMBERS.
BUT THAT'S NOT WHAT'S REALLY BUGGING ME.

I NEVER THOUGHT TO USE THE SIGNAL DEVICE TO CALL THE OTHERS. WHY NOT?

MAYBE I WANTED TO TEST MYSELF AGAINST ALL THE POWERS OF J'ONN, HAL, CLARK AND THE OTHERS.
PROVE THAT ONE MAN CAN TAKE DOWN ALL OF THE SUPER BEINGS.
ALL OF THOSE PEOPLE WHO LIVE IN THE SKY.
ALL OF THE FLIERS.

ALL OF THE ABOVE.
ALL OF THE ABOVE
WRITER: JONATHAN LARSEN
ARTIST: JG JONES
COLORS: PAUL MOUNTS
LETTERS: SAIDA TEMOFONTE
COVER BY: ETHAN VAN SCIVER
AND BRIAN MILLER
EDITOR: BEN ABERNATHY
BATMAN CREATED BY BOB KANE
THE END

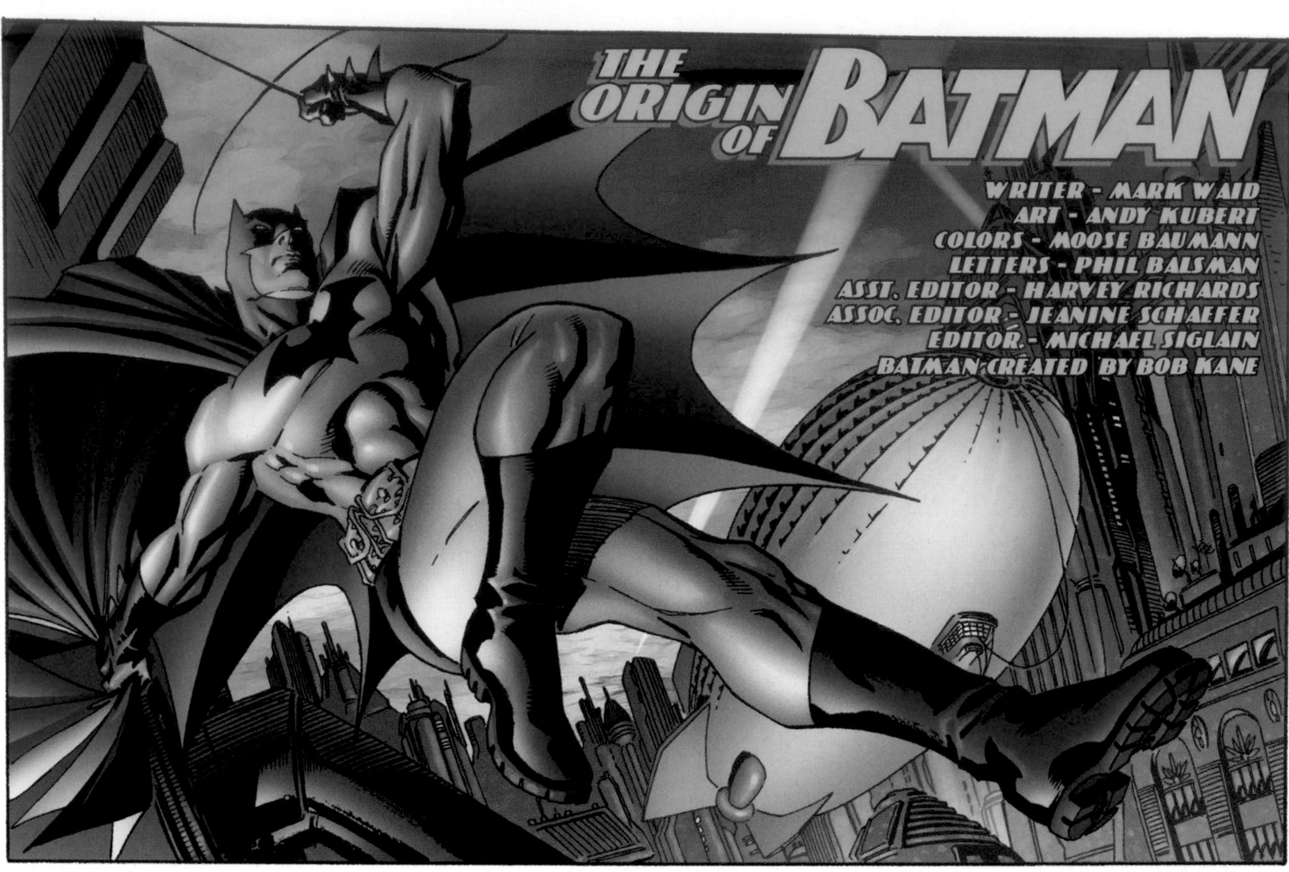
THE ORIGIN OF BATMAN
WRITER - MARK WAID
ART - ANDY KUBERT
COLORS - MOOSE BAUMANN
LETTERS - PHIL BALSMAN
ASST. EDITOR - HARVEY RICHARDS
ASSOC. EDITOR - JEANINE SCHAEFER
EDITOR - MICHAEL SIGLAIN
BATMAN CREATED BY BOB KANE

BRUCE WAYNE LEARNED THE POWER OF FEAR AS A BOY--
--WATCHING IN FROZEN HORROR AS HIS PARENTS, TWO OF GOTHAM CITY'S LEADING CITIZENS, WERE ROBBED AND MURDERED BY A COMMON THUG.

AT THEIR GRAVES, BRUCE SWORE A SOLEMN VOW TO AVENGE THEIR DEATHS.
RELYING LESS UPON HIS BILLION-DOLLAR INHERITANCE THAN ON HIS IRON WILL, BRUCE TRAVELED THE GLOBE--

--GRADUALLY TRAINING HIS MIND AND BODY TO THE PEAK OF HUMAN PERFECTION--
--WHILE STUDYING UNDER THE BEST CRIMINOLOGISTS, DETECTIVES AND FIGHTERS THE WORLD HAD TO OFFER.

## POWERS AND WEAPONS:

Besides being a master of fighting styles, the Batman is a legendary escape artist and the world's greatest detective. His utility belt is stocked with a wide array of tools and armaments, including batarangs, grapnels and zip-lines, gas and smoke capsules, and remote controls for his fleet of Batmobiles.

## ESSENTIAL STORYLINES:

THE BATMAN CHRONICLES
BATMAN: YEAR ONE
THE DARK KNIGHT RETURNS
BATMAN: THE GREATEST STORIES EVER TOLD

## ALLIANCES:

Justice League of America

# DC COMICS MOST WELL KNOWN CHARACTER

I RUN... AND THEN I JUMP OFF! EASY PEASY!

WELL, I'VE BEEN ON SOME PRETTY TALL BUILDINGS IN THE CITY. GREAT VIEW. ONCE I WAS ON ONE AND IT KIND OF... BROKE.

COOKI BREAK!

HAIRBALL IN 3, 2, 1 ...

PUSH THE WIND AWAY!

DC NATION™

DON'T MISS ALL NEW EPISODES ON DC NATION – JANUARY 2013

THE FIRST INCIDENT WAS NEAR MONOLITH SQUARE.
CARVED
WRITER: PAUL TOBIN ARTIST: TRADD MOORE COLORS: REX LOKUS LETTERS: SAIDA TEMOFONTE
COVER: TRADD MOORE ASSOCIATE EDITOR: KRISTY QUINN EDITORS: BEN ABERNATHY AND HANK KANALZ
BATMAN CREATED BY BOB KANE

TANYA ISAACSON WAS TAKING HER BABY DAUGHTER FOR AN EVENING STROLL. THEY NEVER CAME HOME.

BUT A WOODEN STATUE APPEARED IN THEIR PLACE. A CARVED REPLICA OF THE MOTHER. OF THE BABY. EVEN THE DOLL. EVERYTHING.
MAHOGANY. NOT UNCOMMON. GOOD FOR CARVING.

WE'VE ALREADY TAKEN SAMPLES. RUNNING THEM NOW. AND...
...WHO ARE YOU AGAIN?
GORDON SENT ME.
WHY THESE WOODEN DUPLICATES? WHY WERE THESE LEFT BEHIND? WHAT MESSAGE IS THE KIDNAPPER TRYING TO SEND?

AND THEN A SIMILAR INCIDENT, A NIGHT LATER. AN APARTMENT WAS ROBBED. A CHILD AND A TELEVISION WENT MISSING, WITH WOODEN REPLICAS LEFT IN THEIR PLACE.
CAN YOU... PLEASE FIND HIM?

THE NIGHT AFTER THAT, A CONVENIENCE STORE CLERK AND FIVE BOTTLES OF WINE WERE TAKEN. REPLACED BY A WOODEN CLERK. FIVE WOODEN BOTTLES. A WOODEN CELL PHONE.

FIVE MORE INCIDENTS SINCE THEN. A WOODEN DOG. WOODEN SCHOOL-BOOKS. FIVE WOODEN MOTHERS. FIVE WOODEN DAUGHTERS.
GOTHAM... WHAT ARE YOU DOING THIS TIME?

MY ONLY CLUE IS AN EMERGING PATTERN. EACH OF THE CRIMES TOOK PLACE AT A LOCATION VISIBLE FROM THE LAST INCIDENT.
THE PERPETRATOR SEEMS TO HAVE NO PLANNING PAST RANDOMLY LOOKING OUT A WINDOW AND DECIDING WHO TO TAKE NEXT.

IT'S CRAZY. MAKES ME WONDER IF IT'S THE JOKER. WHICH IS UNWISE OF ME.
CAN'T ALWAYS THINK OF THE JOKER WHEN THINGS ARE CRAZY. HALF OF GOTHAM SEEMS CRAZY SOME DAYS.

KNOWING EACH CRIME TAKES PLACE IN SIGHT OF THE LAST, I'VE BEEN RUNNING A CIRCLE OF POSSIBLE HOT POINTS. SIX HOURS OF KEEPING AN EYE ON THE HALF OF GOTHAM THAT ISN'T CRAZY.
AND IT PAYS OFF. THREE MEN UNLOADING A WOODEN STATUE OF A WOMAN. FROM A VAN.
WHY IS IT ALWAYS A VAN?
WHAT THE...?
WHUMP
UUH!
BATMAN!
SHUNK
URGFF!

WHAKT
A TARPAULIN THEY USED TO COVER THE STATUE COMES IN HANDY. HE FIRES SEVEN SHOTS, THINKING IT'S MY CAPE.
I FIRE ONE PUNCH. ONE FIST. INTO A BROKEN THING THAT WAS ONCE A JAW.
CARRYING WALLETS ON A JOB. SLOPPY. UNTHINKING. USUALLY MEANS THEY WON'T KNOW ANYTHING. DEAD ENDS.
AMATEURS.
SO, YOUR NAME IS BERTRAM RYBANDT. OKAY, THEN, RYBANDT, YOU KNOW I'M CONSIDERED PITILESS. IT'S A REPUTATION I'VE EARNED.
ARE YOU GOING TO KEEP THAT IN MIND WHILE I ASK A FEW QUESTIONS?
Y-YES, SIR!

WAYNE MANSION.
"BUT THEY DIDN'T KNOW ANYTHING. JUST HIRED TO MOVE OBJECTS FROM ONE PLACE TO THE NEXT. PAID BY A MONEY DROP. AND I'VE ALREADY TRACED THE WOOD, BUT...

...IT'S THE SAME DEAD END. PAID FOR IN CASH. ANOTHER MONEY DROP. LEFT IN AN ABANDONED PARKING LOT, PER INSTRUCTIONS.
PERHAPS IF YOU CONCENTRATED ON THE PARTY WHILE THE GUESTS ARE HERE, YOU MIGHT GIVE YOUR MIND SOME REST AND--

I KNOW WHERE MY GUESTS ARE, AND I KNOW THERE'S A MADMAN OUT THERE WITH HOSTAGES, AND I KNOW MY PRIORITIES.
BRUCE! BRUCE-YYYY!

HELLO, ROXY, YOU MAGNIFICENT CREATURE! SO... WHY ARE YOU YELLING MY NAME?
NOT THAT I MIND HEARING MY NAME FROM THOSE GORGEOUS LIPS OF YOURS.
STEYA AND I WERE JUST TALKING ABOUT THIS PAINTING! SHE SAYS IT'S CRAP.

WHAT? ROXY! I DID NOT! BRUCE... I DIDN'T!
SHE DID SAY IT'S CRAP...BUT I SAY THERE AREN'T MANY ARTISTS CAPABLE OF SUCH BEAUTY. THERE'S AN INNER MEANING TO THIS THAT...

BRUCE?
BRUCE?
SCORE ONE FOR THE LADIES. I'VE BEEN TOO FOCUSED ON THE SURFACE OF THE CRIME. THE SURFACE OF THE ART. BUT CRIME AND ART... THEY HAVE MEANING.
AND THOSE CARVINGS...? GOTHAM HAS A THRIVING ARTS COMMUNITY. POSSIBLY A HUNDRED ARTISTS CAPABLE OF SUCH A HIGH LEVEL OF CRAFT.
THE POLICE HAVE QUESTIONED THEM ALL. FOUND NO CAUSE FOR SUSPICION. I'VE BEEN DOUBLE-CHECKING INTERCEPTED REPORTS, AND UP UNTIL NOW I'VE AGREED.
ARVER GALLERY
BENJAMIN CARVER
APPOINTMENTS ONLY
BUT NOW, IN THESE REPORTS, I'M NOT LOOKING FOR CRIMINAL BACKGROUNDS OR ANYTHING OF THAT SORT.

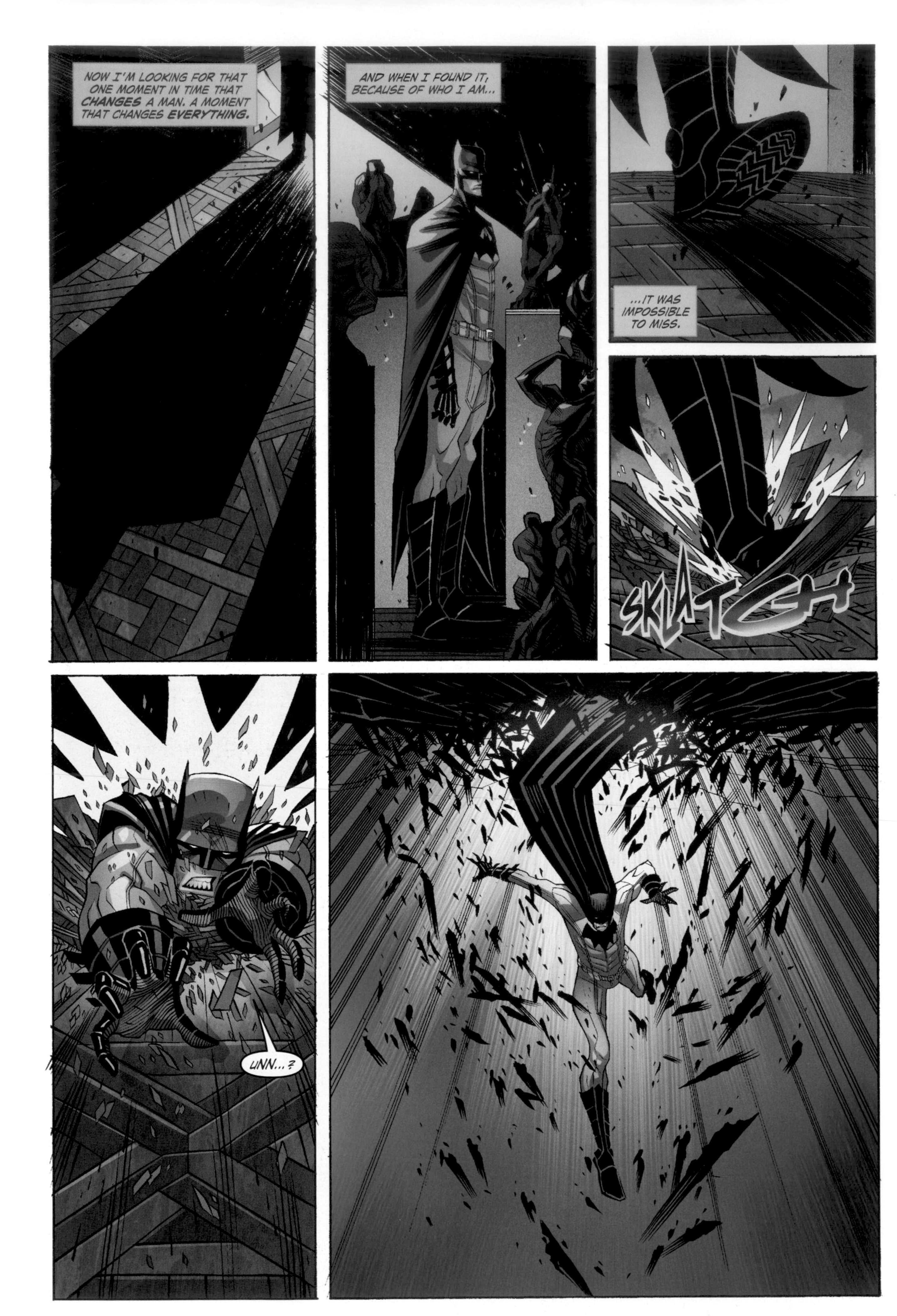
NOW I'M LOOKING FOR THAT ONE MOMENT IN TIME THAT CHANGES A MAN. A MOMENT THAT CHANGES EVERYTHING.
AND WHEN I FOUND IT, BECAUSE OF WHO I AM...
...IT WAS IMPOSSIBLE TO MISS.
SKLATCH
UNN...?

STOP! D-DON'T... DON'T MOVE!
A GUN.

YES. A GUN. BECAUSE I KNEW YOU WOULD COME FOR ME.
KNEW YOU WOULD UNDERSTAND THAT ONLY MY ARTISTRY COULD DO WHAT HAS BEEN DONE.
NOW, REMEMBER, BEFORE YOU THINK OF ATTACKING ME, YOU SHOULD UNDERSTAND MY ART. YOU SHOULD UNDERSTAND WHY I'VE DONE ALL THIS.

AND YOU SHOULD UNDERSTAND I HAVE HOSTAGES WHO WILL DIE UNLESS YOU DO WHAT I SAY.
WHAT DO YOU WANT?

"WHAT DO I WANT? I WANT MY WIFE AND DAUGHTER. ALIVE. I WANT THEM BACK. THIS CITY TOOK THEM FROM ME.

"THIS CITY TURNED THEM INTO WOOD."

I CAN'T BRING THE DEAD BACK TO LIFE. NOBODY CAN.
BIP
WRONG! YOU HEROES...YOU DIE ALL THE TIME! AND YOU COME BACK! YOU BRING MY FAMILY BACK OR I'LL TURN EVERYONE TO--

UUH!
WHACK

NO! DON'T YOU UNDERSTAND? I HAVE HOSTAGES! HIDDEN! THEY'LL DIE IF I DON'T TELL YOU WHERE THEY ARE!
THEY'LL TURN TO WOOD! WOOD IN THE GROUND!
DON'T YOU UNDERSTAND?

KRAK
I UNDERSTAND MORE THAN YOU CAN POSSIBLY IMAGINE.

GUHH!
WHACK

UUUH!
SMAK

ON THE WAY HERE TO YOUR GALLERY, I *RESEARCHED* YOUR LIFE. *STUDIED* WHAT HAPPENED TO YOU. STUDIED HOW YOU *COULDN'T LET GO.*
I *UNDERSTAND* YOU. I UNDERSTAND HOW YOU *THINK.*

"I CONTACTED COMMISSIONER GORDON. TOLD THE POLICE TO LOOK FOR THE HOSTAGES IN THE GRAVEYARD, BURIED NEXT TO YOUR FAMILY."
THEY'RE *HERE! ALIVE!*

GORDON SENT ME A SIGNAL. TOLD ME THEY'D BEEN FOUND.
B-BUT... HOW...HOW COULD YOU KNOW WHERE TO LOOK?
BECAUSE I KNOW HOW HARD IT IS TO LET GO. BECAUSE I KNEW YOU'D KEEP THE HOSTAGES CLOSE TO YOUR GREATEST PAIN.
BECAUSE YOU'RE NOT THE ONLY ONE WHO MISSES HIS FAMILY.
THE END

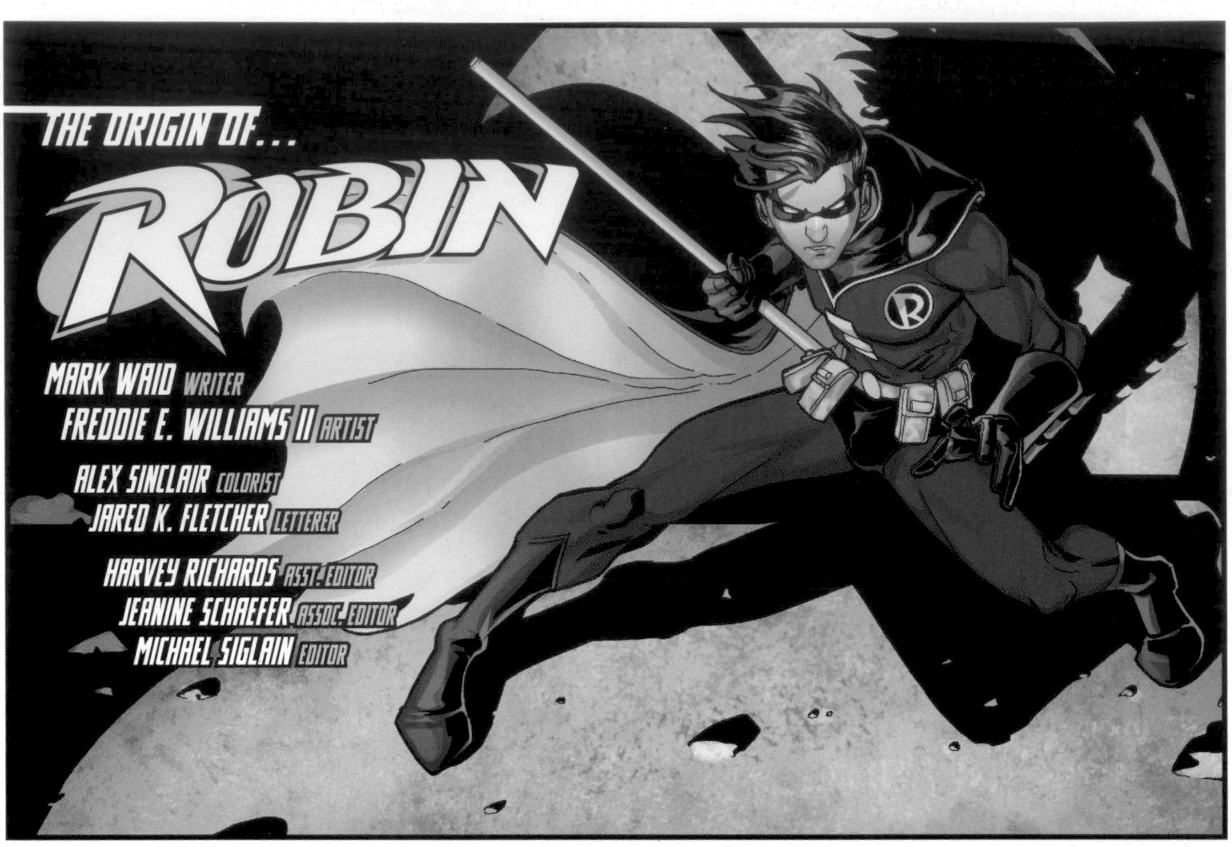
THE ORIGIN OF...
ROBIN
MARK WAID WRITER
FREDDIE E. WILLIAMS II ARTIST
ALEX SINCLAIR COLORIST
JARED K. FLETCHER LETTERER
HARVEY RICHARDS ASST. EDITOR
JEANINE SCHAEFER ASSOC. EDITOR
MICHAEL SIGLAIN EDITOR

THE EYES OF A FAN CAUGHT A MOMENT THE REST OF THE WORLD HAD OVERLOOKED.
TIM DRAKE-- AND TIM DRAKE ALONE-- HAD GROWN UP FASCINATED BY THE CAREER OF AN OBSCURE AND FORGOTTEN CHILD ACROBAT NAMED DICK GRAYSON--
--BUT WHEN TIM SAW BATMAN'S PARTNER ROBIN PERFORM GRAYSON'S SIGNATURE GYMNASTIC MOVES, SOMETHING CLICKED IN TIM'S MIND.

OVER THE NEXT FEW YEARS, TIM-- THROUGH A SERIES OF CLUES AND LUCKY BREAKS-- PROVED CONCLUSIVELY THAT GRAYSON WAS ROBIN...
...OR, RATHER, HAD BEEN.

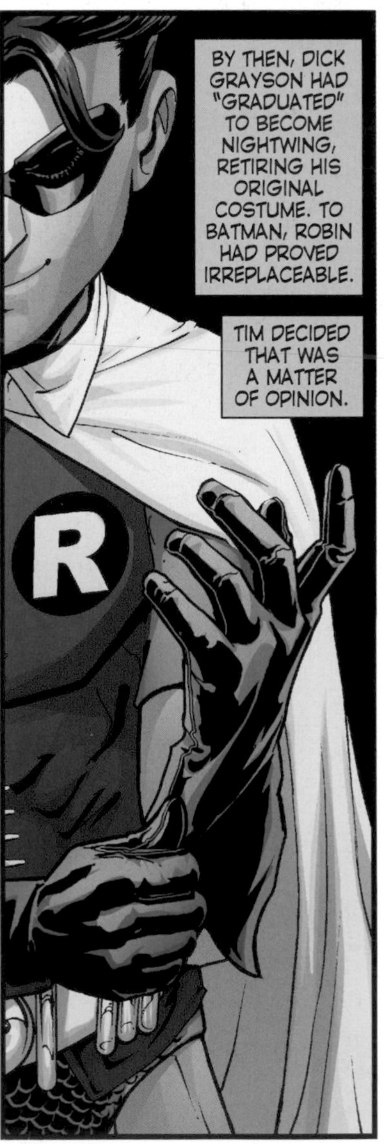
BY THEN, DICK GRAYSON HAD "GRADUATED" TO BECOME NIGHTWING, RETIRING HIS ORIGINAL COSTUME. TO BATMAN, ROBIN HAD PROVED IRREPLACEABLE.
TIM DECIDED THAT WAS A MATTER OF OPINION.

## POWERS AND WEAPONS:

Besides being a skilled detective and acrobat, Robin carries a mini-arsenal of devices including a collapsible bo staff, "R"-shaped shurikens, and a utility belt filled with gas pellets and other traditional bat-gadgets.

## ESSENTIAL STORYLINES:

- BATMAN: YEAR THREE
- ROBIN: A HERO REBORN
- ROBIN: TRAGEDY AND TRIUMPH
- IDENTITY CRISIS

## ALLIANCES:

Teen Titans

I USED TO LOVE THE RAIN.
I'D LAY IN BED AT NIGHT LISTENING TO IT PATTER ON THE ROOF ABOVE ME.
IT MADE ME FEEL SAFE.
AT PEACE.
SPLUT
BUT THAT WAS BEFORE I UNDERSTOOD THERE IS NO SUCH THING AS PEACE...
THERE IS ONLY WAR.

CRIMINALS AREN'T MUCH DIFFERENT FROM RATS.
THEY SKITTER FROM THE DARKNESS AND TAKE WHATEVER THEY WANT.
WHEN A NEW PREDATOR IS INTRODUCED INTO THEIR HABITAT, THE RATS HAVE A CHOICE...
...DIE.
OR ADAPT.
IT'S BEEN SIX MONTHS SINCE THEY FIRST SAW ME.
AND IT'S TAKEN THEM SIX MONTHS TO ABANDON THEIR NESTS.
THEY'RE LEARNING.
BUT I'M LEARNING, TOO.

I CHANGE MY PATTERNS.
I HUNT FROM ABOVE.

THIS IS WHAT KEEPS ME AT THE TOP OF THE FOOD CHAIN.
INTELLIGENCE.
WHUP!
UNPREDICTABILITY.
DEVOTION TO MY CAUSE.

THIS IS WHY I WILL ALWAYS FIND THEM.
THIS IS WHY I AM SUPERI--

...NO.
NOT AGAIN.

NOT THIS TIME.

LISTEN TO ME.
I'M GOING TO BEAT YOU UNTIL YOU'RE UNCONSCIOUS.
WHILE I DO THAT, I WANT YOU TO REPEAT SOMETHING TO YOURSELF.
"NO FAMILIES.
"NO KIDS."

THAT AIN'T NO KID, YOU IDIOT.

THWUUU

TRAP...
DAMMIT...
WALKED...
RIGHT...
INTO...
IT...
STAGED...
JUST...
FOR...
ME...
MOTHER...
FATHER...
SON...
HOW...
COULD...
THEY...
KNOW...
WHO...
I...
AM?
THESE ARE JUST THUGS...
...SOMEONE HIRED THEM...
...ONE OF THE PSYCHOPATHS WHO DRESSES UP LIKE A FREAK...
...ONE OF THEM FOUND OUT WHO I AM.
USED IT AGAINST ME...
...MADE ME SLOPPY...
WHICH ONE?
WHICH ONE KNOWS ABOUT THE NIGHT I WAS BORN?
WHICH ONE IS SICK ENOUGH TO USE MY PARENTS' MURDER TO--?
--OH.
NO.
IT COULDN'T BE...

NO VULNERABILITY.

PARDON ME, SIR?
THAT'S WHAT SEPARATES ME FROM THEM.
WHAT MAKES ME BETTER.

I CAN'T FLY OR RUN FAST...
...I DON'T HAVE A MAGIC RING THAT MAKES GIANT GREEN...

...IMAGINARY STUFF...

...DO YOU KNOW WHAT I'D DO WITH THAT RING?
WHAT I'D IMAGINE?
PERHAPS YOU'VE HAD ENOUGH TO DRINK, MASTER BRUCE.

YEAH, THEY'VE GOT POWERS.
BUT POWERS COME WITH WEAKNESSES.

LIKE KRYPTONITE. OR THE COLOR YELLOW.
...YELLOW.
GOD FORBID HE HAS TO SLOW DOWN AT A TRAFFIC LIGHT.

SIR, IT'S BEEN A LONG NIGHT. LET ME DRAW YOU A HOT BA--

YOU KNOW WHAT MY WEAKNESS IS?

I DON'T HAVE ONE.
THAT'S WHAT MAKES ME BETTER THAN THEM.

THAT'S WHY I'LL ALWAYS WIN.

NO VULNERABILITY.

YOUR SILENCE INFERS DISAPPROVAL.

IT *IMPLIES* DISAPPROVAL.

YOU AND THE GRAMMAR.

THE GRAMMAR AND I, SIR.
IF YOU HAVE SOMETHING TO SAY, ALFRED, SAY IT.
EVERYONE HAS A VULNERABILITY.

NOT ME.

I ASSURE YOU, MASTER BRUCE, THAT YOU DO.
I'LL BET YOU A DOLLAR I DON'T.
A GENTLEMAN NEVER ACCEPTS A WAGER FROM A DRUNKARD.

I'M ONLY PRETENDING TO BE DRUNK.
THAT'S THE ACT, REMEMBER?

*IS* IT AN ACT, SIR?
ONE DOLLAR.
RIGHT HERE. RIGHT NOW.

JUST TELL ME MY VULNERABILITY.
TELL ME WHAT MY WEAKNESS IS.

THAT'S WHAT I THOUGHT.

THAT WILL BE QUITE ENOUGH, THANK YOU.

GOOD EVENING, MASTER BRUCE.

# THE BUTLER DID IT

Writer: Damon Lindelof
Artist: Jeff Lemire
Colors: Jose Villarubia
Letters: Saida Temofonte

# THE BATMOBILE: COOLEST CAR EVER?

**Batman's ride sure has changed over the years! Which one is YOUR favorite?**

## *Batman TV Series* (1966)

**Batphone**

**Batscope**

**Bat-turn lever, which pops bat-chutes**

**Chain-slicer or Bat-ram**

**Bat-computer**

**Batray reactors and laser beams**

**Bat smoke screen**

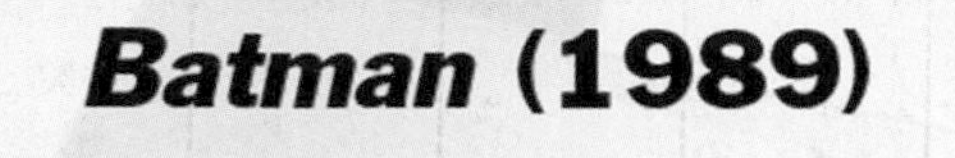

## *Batman* (1989)

Grappling hook for high-speed turns

Twin Browning submachine guns that rise from the body of the Batmobile

Grenades deployed from the center of the wheels

Full body armor that is bulletproof and fireproof

Oil slick dispensers

Smoke dispensers

Fenders and fins create a Bat wing or Batman's cape effect.

Illuminated hubcaps that stayed static while the car was in motion so the Bat symbol would always be seen upright.

When fired at full capacity, shoots a 25-foot flame out of the rear exhaust.

## *atman Forever* (1995)

Batman and Robin
(1997)
Onboard Voice-
activated Computer
Dual-mount sub carriage rocket launchers
Multipoint infrared and laser scan
Tracking units
Catapult ejection seat
Silent Mode allows Batman to switch to electric
power and navigate via night vision. Typically
used to evade both enemies and police.
Attack mode, which transports Batman to the
center of the vehicle for better maneuverability.
Caltrops, which were rope mines released
to explode behind the Batmobile
and disable pursuing vehicles.
Auto cannons
Armor plating
The Dark Knight Trilogy
(2005-2012)
DC
NATION™

The blizzard took out Gotham like a fly in a tornado. Power's down.

All but the most inept villains have escaped and are at large.

# BATMAN IN SNOW PATROL

WRITTEN BY STEVE NILES
ART BY STEPHANIE BUSCEMA
LETTERS BY JOHN J. HILL

NOW.
RRAAOOR!!

THEN.
AT FIRST WE THOUGHT IT WAS A JOKE, LIKE ALLIGATORS IN THE SEWERS. THAT'S WHAT PEEPS SAID WAS LURKING AROUND. JUST STORIES, WE THOUGHT-- BUT THEN...THEN...
PEOPLE STARTED TO DISAPPEAR.
YEAH, NOT THAT ANYONE CARED. HOMELESS GOES MISSING, WHO EVEN NOTICES?
BUT THEN...THEN AFTER A FEW MORE OF US GONE AND THE BLOOD...I SAW IT. THE THING HAD WINGS. NOT LIKE YOURS, BUT LIKE A--A DRAGON!
GET TO A SHELTER. DON'T COME OUT UNTIL YOU HEAR IT'S SAFE.
SAFE? YOU AIN'T NEVER BEEN TO A SHELTER IN GOTHAM!

THE ATTACKS ALL HAPPENED WITHIN THESE SIX BLOCKS.

BUT IT HASN'T LEFT A TRAIL LIKE THIS BEFORE. SOMETHING'S CHANGED.
IT WAS FLYING BEFORE, LEAVING NO TRACKS.

BUT NOW ITS PATH IS CLEAR.

A SCALE OF SOME KIND WAS LEFT AT ONE OF THE ATTACKS.
MY ANALYSIS SHOWED THAT IT'S FROM AN UNIDENTIFIED REPTILE.
I JUST IDENTIFIED IT.
FTTSSSH
BUT A DRAGON IN GOTHAM?

THERE'S GOT TO BE MORE TO THIS RIDDLE.
I'LL FIGURE THAT OUT WHEN I BRING IT IN.

I DON'T WANT TO HURT IT.
I DOUBT THE FEELING IS MUTUAL.
RRRAAR!

ESPECIALLY AFTER INJECTING IT WITH A NEEDLE THIS BIG--
KK

THUD

ALWAYS HAVE A BACKUP PLAN.

THE NET CHARGE IS RISKIER, THOUGH.
KLKT

MY INSULATED SUIT PROTECTS ME FROM THE SHOCK.
BUT IT COULD SEND THE BEAST INTO CARDIAC ARREST FOR ALL I KNOW.

IT'S DOING FINE. I ONLY MADE IT ANGRIER.

KAFOOSH

LET'S SEE... WHAT ELSE YOU GOT, BRUCE?

THE NETTING, TRANQUILIZERS, AND TASER ALL FAILED.
LET'S JUST DO THIS THE HARD WAY, THEN.
WHEN IT LUNGES AT ME I REALIZE SOMETHING IS WRONG.
WHATEVER THIS MONSTER IS, IT'S SICK--BURNING WITH SOME BILE DESTROYING IT FROM THE INSIDE.
I CAN SMELL IT.
THE SICKNESS IS MAKING IT WEAK, OFF-BALANCE.
I CAN TAKE ADVANTAGE OF THAT...
...THEN CAPTURE IT ALIVE.

SICK OR NOT, THIS THING IS STILL FAST.
IF THE NETTING WON'T HOLD HIM...
...MAYBE THIS KEVLAR WILL.
THWACK!
KROAAR!
OOF!

KKKRSH H
A POWER LINE. LUCKY.
LUCK IS THE WORST PLAN, BUT IT'S ALL I'VE GOT NOW.
THAT'S ENOUGH POWER TO LIGHT UP A CITY BLOCK.
OR KILL A DRAGON.
BUT BEAST OR NOT...
...I WON'T LET THE THING JUST DIE.
AAHK!

TWO PREDATORS FIGHTING FOR THEIR LIVES.
DRAGON VERSUS BAT.
BAT LOSES.
KRRAACK
BETTER MAKE THAT THREE PREDATORS.
KILLER CROC!

WHAT HAPPENED?!
W-WITHOUT ITS TREATMENT, THE C-CREATURE'S IMMUNE SYSTEM TURNED ON ITSELF. ITS CELLS WERE BREAKING DOWN... DROVE IT INTO A-A RABID STAGE...
YOU DID THIS, CROC?
I MADE IT. I WANTED A THING OF MY OWN. TO BE MORE THAN AN ANIMAL.
I JUST WANTED...
RRAAOOR!!
WHAT KIND OF FAMILY COULD A MONSTER HAVE?

WE'RE JUST MONSTERS-- ALL OF US.
YOU TRIED TO SAVE IT.
I'LL KILL YOU NEXT TIME.
TAKE THE MAN. LEAVE ME ALONE.
N-NO... NO... WAIT--
KILLER CROC WAS TRYING TO REACH HIS HUMAN SIDE--TO BE MORE THAN A BEAST.
BUT IN SPARING TWO INNOCENT LIVES TODAY HE SHOWED A LITTLE HUMANITY.
PERHAPS ONE DAY HE'LL REALIZE THAT...
...THERE IS ALWAYS HOPE.